KOYOHARU GOTOUGE

They're publishing a graphic novel by me! Thank you! And heartfelt thanks to all the readers, my editors over the years, my assistants, everyone in the *Jump* editorial department, everyone at the printer, the people who designed the book, and the many other people who have offered their help!

DEMON SLAYER: KIMETSU NO YAIBA VOLUME 1
Shonen Jump Edition

Story and Art by
KOYOHARU GOTOUGE

KIMETSU NO YAIBA
© 2016 by Koyoharu Gotouge
All rights reserved. First published in Japan
in 2016 by SHUEISHA Inc., Tokyo. English
translation rights arranged by SHUEISHA Inc.

TRANSLATION John Werry
ENGLISH ADAPTATION Stan!
TOUCH-UP ART & LETTERING John Hunt
DESIGN Adam Grano
EDITOR Mike Montesa

Printed in Italy

Published by VIZ Media, LLC
P.O. Box 77010
San Francisco, CA 94107

33
First printing, July 2018
Thirty-third printing, July 2024

viz.com

CRUELTY

DEMON
SLAYER
KIMETSU NO YAIBA

KOYOHARU
GOTOUGE

CONTENTS

DEMON SLAYER
KIMETSU NO YAIBA

1

CRUELTY

CHAPTER 1: CRUELTY

TANJIRO!

YOU DON'T HAVE TO GO.

IT'S SNOWING AND IT'S DANGEROUS.

YOUR FACE IS PITCH-BLACK.

COME HERE.

THANK YOU.

...EVEN IF IT'S JUST A LITTLE.

I WANT US TO HAVE A GREAT NEW YEAR'S FEAST, SO I'LL GO SELL AS MUCH CHARCOAL AS I CAN...

WHAAAAA?!

I WANNA GO TOO!

TANJIRO, ARE YOU GOING TO TOWN AGAIN TODAY?

...SO HE CAN'T PULL YOU WHEN YOU'RE TIRED.

HE ISN'T TAKING THE CART TODAY...

BUT MOM!

NO.

NO. YOU CAN'T WALK FAST LIKE TANJIRO.

I WILL, BUT...

...I WAS HOPING WE'D DO IT TOGETHER.

I wanna go with you!

TAKEO...

I KNOW YOU CAN'T DO A LOT, BUT CUT A LITTLE WOOD TODAY. OKAY?

BE CARE-FUL!

HURRY BACK, OKAY?

I WAS PUTTING ROKUTA TO SLEEP...

NEZUKO...

...BUT I HEARD ALL THE COMMOTION.

TANJIRO!

SEE YOU LATER!

...SO THEY'VE STARTED CLINGING TO YOU.

THEY'VE BEEN SO LONELY SINCE FATHER DIED...

IT'S ALWAYS CHANGING.

BUT LIFE IS LIKE THE WEATHER...

...AND THE SNOW WON'T ALWAYS KEEP FALLING.

IT WON'T ALWAYS BE EASY...

...THE SMELL OF BLOOD IN THE AIR.

WHEN HAPPINESS ENDS THERE'S ALWAYS...

OUR LIFE ISN'T EASY, BUT WE'RE HAPPY.

OH, TANJIRO!

THANKS FOR FIXING MY SHOJI DOOR THE OTHER DAY!

YOU'LL CATCH A COLD!

YOU CAME DOWN THE MOUNTAIN ON A DAY LIKE TODAY? YOU WORK SO HARD!

GIVE ME SOME CHARCOAL TOO!

HEY! SELL ME SOME CHARCOAL!

HELP ME!

SMELL IT!

SHE SAYS I BROKE A DISH!

YOU'RE JUST IN TIME!

AAAH! TANJIRO!

WILL YOU HELP ME CARRY SOME BUNDLES?!

TANJIRO!

I TOLD YOU IT WASN'T ME!

A CAT? OH DEAR.

I SMELL A CAT.

SEEEE ?!

WHEW! IT'S GETTING LATE!

TP TP TP

IT'S TOO DANGER-OUS!

HEY, TAN-JIRO! YOU AREN'T...

...GOING BACK UP THE MOUNTAIN ARE YOU?!

14

BUT...

IT'S ALL RIGHT. YOU'RE WELCOME HERE.

YOU CAN STAY HERE.

COME BACK.

PLEASE.

I'VE GOT A GOOD NOSE FOR TROUBLE. I'LL BE FINE.

YOU DON'T WANT TO RUN INTO ANY *DEMONS*.

SO YOU SHOULDN'T WALK AROUND AT NIGHT.

EAT, THEN SLEEP. YOU CAN GET UP AND GO HOME EARLY TOMORROW.

... MAN-EATING DEMONS HAVE ROAMED THESE WOODS AFTER DARK.

FOR AGES...

YES...

...THEY CAN.

CAN'T THE DEMONS COME INSIDE HOUSES?

BUT...

BECAUSE *DEMON SLAYERS* CUT THEM DOWN.

HAVE FOR AGES...

...WHY DON'T THEY EAT EVERY-ONE?

... THEN ...

BUT...

THERE'S NO NEED TO FEAR. THERE'S NO SUCH THING AS DEMONS.

BUT NOW THAT I THINK OF IT...

NEXT TIME, I'LL BRING MY LITTLE BROTHERS.

OLD MAN SABURO LIVES ALONE BECAUSE HE LOST HIS FAMILY. HE MUST BE LONELY.

...MY GRANDMOTHER SAID THE SAME THING BEFORE SHE DIED.

WHEN HAPPINESS ENDS THERE'S ALWAYS...

...THE SMELL OF BLOOD IN THE AIR.

HFF

HFF

WHAT HAP—

WHAT HAPPENED P!

AGH!

WHAT THE...?

NEZUKO
...

ROKUTA
...

TAKEO...

SHIGERU
...

MOTHER
...

HANAKO
...

ONLY NEZUKO'S BODY WAS STILL WARM.

MAYBE A DOCTOR CAN SAVE HER.

HOW DID THIS HAPPEN? A BEAR?

MAYBE A BEAR TOO HUNGRY TO HIBERNATE?

BUT IT ALSO MADE ME SLIP!

THE SNOW...

...SAVED ME.

SHWF

NEZUKO!

!!

YOU SHOULDN'T BE UP!

...CARRY YOU INTO TOWN!

LET ME...

NEZUKO!

ARE YOU ALL RIGHT?

SHF

NEZUKO...

WH
MPH

OMP

CH

I THOUGHT OF WHAT OLD MAN SABURO SAID.

WAS NEZUKO...

...A MAN-EATING DEMON?

A DEMON!

NEZUKO HAS BEEN HUMAN...

...SINCE THE DAY SHE WAS BORN.

NO, THAT WAS IM-POSSIBLE.

...FALLEN OVER ROKUTA, LIKE SHE WAS PROTECTING HIM.

BUT NEZUKO COULDN'T HAVE DONE ALL THAT. I FOUND HER...

BUT THIS NEZUKO...

...SMELLS OF BLOOD AND DEATH.

WHOOMP

SHE DIDN'T HAVE ANY BLOOD ON HER MOUTH OR HANDS.

AND THERE'S YET...

SKRR

SHFF

SKRK

...AN-OTHER SMELL...

KRK

KRK

...AND SHE'S GETTING STRONGER!

...SHE'S GROWING BIGGER...

WHATEVER THE REASON...

...HAPPENED TO MY WHOLE FAMILY.

WHILE I WAS SAFELY ASLEEP IN TOWN, SOMETHING HORRIBLE...

BUT SHE'S SO STRONG! I CAN'T PUSH HER AWAY!

KRK

I HAVE TO SAVE NEZUKO IF I CAN!

NEZUKO!

KRK

HOW THEY MUST HAVE SUFFERED.

...AND I WASN'T THERE TO HELP THEM.

BE STRONG!

YOU CAN DO IT!

DON'T TURN INTO A DEMON!

HOLD ON, NEZUKO!

FIGHT IT! FIGHT FOR YOUR LIFE!

PLIP

PLIP

PLIP

NEZUKO!

GRAAAR

S-SISTER...

SHE'S MY...

...LITTLE SISTER!

THAT IS YOUR LITTLE SISTER?

GRAH

RAAGH

SNATCH

DASH

...

GRAAAH!

NEZUKO!

HWSH !

DON'T MOVE.

WAIT! NEZUKO HASN'T KILLED ANYONE!

SO OF COURSE, I'LL TAKE YOUR LITTLE SISTER'S HEAD TOO.

KILLING DEMONS IS MY JOB.

THAT MUST BE WHO KILLED EVERYONE!

...FROM SOMEONE I'VE NEVER SMELLED BEFORE!

THERE WAS A SCENT AT MY HOUSE...

THAT'S EASY. DEMON BLOOD GOT IN HER WOUND, SO SHE'S TRANSFORMED INTO A DEMON.

GRAAR!

BUT...

NOT NEZUKO!

I DON'T KNOW WHAT'S MAKING HER ACT LIKE THIS...

THAT IS HOW MAN-EATING DEMONS MULTIPLY.

NO! I'M SURE SHE KNOWS WHO I AM!

A MOMENT AGO SHE ALMOST ATE *YOU!*

NEZUKO WOULD NEVER EAT ANYONE!

I'LL FIND A WAY TO *CURE* HER!

I'LL MAKE HER *HUMAN* AGAIN!

I *WON'T* LET HER HURT ANYONE!

I'LL FIND A WAY! I SWEAR! PLEASE DON'T KILL HER!

A HUMAN WHO BECOMES A DEMON CANNOT GO BACK.

SHE WON'T GET BETTER.

SH NNG

...SO...

...SO...

I'LL ALSO FIND THE ONE THAT KILLED MY FAMILY!

I'LL DO ALL THAT, SO...

I CAN'T LOSE NEZUKO TOO!

STOP!

PLEASE, STOP.

PLEASE...

PLEASE DON'T KILL MY LITTLE SISTER!

PLEASE...

38

...CURE HIS LITTLE SISTER?

OR EVEN *FIND* HIS ENEMY?

HOW CAN A WEAKLING LIKE YOU, WHO BOWS DOWN WHEN IT'S TIME TO FIGHT, TO KILL OR BE KILLED... HOW CAN SUCH A MAN...

...*YOU MUST FIGHT FOR IT!*

IF YOU WANT SOME-THING...

DEMONS MIGHT KNOW HOW TO CURE YOUR LITTLE SISTER...

...NO DEMON WILL RESPECT YOUR WHINING AND BEGGING!

... BUT ...

THE MEEK HAVE NO POWER AND NO OPTIONS!

THE STRONG WILL CRUSH THEM IN EVERY WAY!

YOUR HEART IS CRUSHED.

YOUR FAMILY IS DEAD AND YOUR SISTER HAS BECOME A DEMON.

I KNOW YOUR PAIN, HOW YOU MUST WANT TO CRY OUT.

DON'T CRY.

DON'T DESPAIR.

THOSE THINGS WILL DO YOU NO GOOD.

BUT THERE IS NO TURNING BACK TIME.

...YOUR FAMILY MIGHT HAVE SURVIVED.

IF I'D COME HALF A DAY SOONER...

ANGER THAT BECOMES THE UNWAVERING FORCE THAT DRIVES YOUR LIMBS.

...THAT GIVES NO QUARTER.

STRONG, PURE ANGER...

FILL YOUR HEART WITH ANGER.

...CANNOT PROTECT YOUR SISTER OR FIND HER A CURE.

WEAKNESS AND EMPTY PROMISES ...

AND THEY CERTAINLY CANNOT AVENGE YOUR FAMILY.

W...

SH NK

AAAAH!

WHOK

WHAT A FOOL!

A SIMPLE, HEAD-ON ATTACK RELYING ON PURE EMOTION.

THOK

JUST BEFORE PASSING BEHIND THE TREE, HE THREW A ROCK...

...AND WHILE HIDDEN BY THE TREE HE THREW HIS HATCHET.

...WAS TO STRIKE ME DOWN AFTER I KILLED HIM.

HE KNEW HE COULDN'T WIN AGAINST ME, SO HIS PLAN...

HE HID HIS HAND SO I WOULDN'T SEE HE WAS UNARMED.

GRAAR!

THIS KID...

WHOK

50

NO! I'M TOO LATE!

SKFF

SHE'S ABOUT TO EAT HIM!

NEZUKO...

NEZUKO WOULD NEVER EAT ANYONE!

NOT NEZUKO!

HE WOULDN'T BE...

...THE FIRST TO SAY THAT AND THEN GET EATEN ANYWAY.

BECAUSE THEY NEED THE ENERGY.

I'VE SEEN IT COUNTLESS TIMES.

STARVING DEMONS WILL KILL AND EAT THEIR OWN PARENTS AND SIBLINGS.

...AND MUST WANT TO EAT HUMAN FLESH AS SOON AS POSSIBLE.

...NOT TO MENTION THE STRENGTH IT TOOK TO TRANSFORM INTO A DEMON. SHE MUST BE DOUBLY STARVED RIGHT NOW...

THIS GIRL IS INJURED. IT COSTS HER STRENGTH...

...TO HEAL THAT WOUND...

...AND FOCUSING HER ANGER ON ME.

BUT SHE'S PROTECTING HIM...

I'M SORRY I HAD TO LEAVE YOU, TANJIRO.

TAKE CARE OF NEZUKO.

HWSH

YOU'RE AWAKE?

HMMPH

TELL HIM THAT *GIYU TOMIOKA* SENT YOU.

GO SEE AN OLD MAN NAMED *SAKONJI UROKODAKI* WHO LIVES AT THE FOOT OF MOUNT SAGIRI.

WHSH

...BUT DON'T LET HER INTO DIRECT SUNLIGHT.

YOUR SISTER SHOULD BE FINE BECAUSE THE SUN ISN'T OUT TODAY...

CHAPTER 2: THE STRANGER

...AND A LITTLE STRAW AND BAMBOO?

I BEG YOUR PARDON...

...BUT MAY I TAKE THAT BASKET...

THAT'S ALL RIGHT. CAN I PAY YOU?

NO NEED. IT'S A BROKEN BASKET.

...BUT THE BASKET HAS A HOLE IN IT.

WE DON'T MIND...

WE DON'T WANT IT!

BUT I *WANT* TO PAY!

WHAT A STUBBORN KID!

NO, THANK YOU.

SHAKE SHAKE

PLEASE LET ME PAY.

YOU CAN HAVE THE OTHER STUFF TOO.

...

THERE SHE IS!

POP

JUST WAIT.

SHE MUST REALLY NOT WANT THE SUNLIGHT TO HIT HER.

HER FACE IS SCRUNCHED UP.

MY SISTER IS LIKE A MOLE NOW.

DID SHE DIG THAT HOLE?

TA-DAH!

FWIK

FWIK

FWIK

...

GET IN.

HERE.

THE BASKET.

I WANT US TO TRAVEL DURING THE DAY.

I'LL CARRY YOU.

WILL YOU FIT IN HERE?

NEZUKO HAS GROWN UP.

I STILL THINK SHE'S A LITTLE GIRL.

YOU'RE TOO BIG.

...RE-VERSE THAT...

...AND GET SMALLER?

NEZUKO...

...YOU'RE AS BIG AS AN ADULT. CAN YOU...

HMM?

KAW
KAW

GOOD GIRL, NEZUKO!

I'M IMPRESSED!

PAT PAT

THAT'S PERFECT!

THE SUN WILL SET SOON.

AND YOU'RE GOING TO CARRY THAT HUGE LOAD? IT'S DANGEROUS.

TO GET TO MOUNT SAGIRI, YOU FIRST HAVE TO CROSS THAT MOUNTAIN.

...SO DON'T GET LOST!

PEOPLE REALLY DO DISAPPEAR UP THERE...

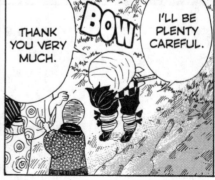

THANK YOU VERY MUCH.

BOW

I'LL BE PLENTY CAREFUL.

OH!

!!

I SMELL BLOOD!

THERE'S A WAY STATION.

THERE'S A LIGHT ON. SOMEONE MUST BE THERE.

LET'S GO.

ARE YOU ALL RIGHT?

THESE MOUNTAIN PATHS ARE DANGEROUS. THAT TRAVELER MAY BE INJURED!

KLAK

KT K

HMM...?

SOMETHING'S WRONG HERE.

PLIP PLIP

A MAN-EATING DEMON!

ARE YOU TWO HUMAN?

SH-SHE JUST KILLED HIM! WELL, HE WAS A DEMON, SO...

WHY YOUUU...!

I CAN'T BELIEVE IT! IT JUST MOVED WITH ITS HEAD RIPPED OFF!

WHAT ARE A DEMON AND A HUMAN DOING TOGETHER?!

I KNEW IT! ONE OF YOU IS A DEMON!

SOMETHING DIDN'T SEEM RIGHT!

TMP TMP TMP

IT'S STILL TALK-ING!!

STOP!

MY HAIR IS TANGLED UP ON THE HAFT! AND I GREW THESE HANDS TOO SHORT, SO I CAN'T GET A GRIP!

ARGH!

HE PINNED ME TO THE TREE WITH HIS HATCHET!

WHSH

NEZUKO!

GYAAAH!

SPLAT

WOW!

SHNG

HOW MANY DEMONS ARE THERE?

SO I HAVE TO DO THIS.

HFF *HFF*

BUT...

...IF I DON'T KILL HIM, HE'LL ATTACK MORE PEOPLE.

HFF *HFF*

A DIFFERENT DEMON.

HE SMELLS DIFFERENT THAN THE ONE THAT WAS AT MY HOUSE.

DO IT!

...LORD SAKONJI UROKODAKI.

GREETINGS...

A DEMON SLAUGHTERED HIS FAMILY...

HE HAD THE COURAGE TO FIGHT ME UNARMED.

I HAVE SENT A BOY YOUR WAY WHO SAYS HE WANTS TO BECOME A DEMON-SLAYING SWORDSMAN.

...BUT SHE CHOOSES NOT TO ATTACK HUMANS.

...TRANSFORMING HIS SURVIVING SISTER INTO A DEMON...

I BELIEVE THAT PERHAPS ...

LIKE YOU, THE BOY HAS A STRONG SENSE OF SMELL.

I SENSE SOMETHING IN THESE TWO THAT IS DIFFERENT FROM THE OTHERS.

I KNOW THIS IS A SELFISH REQUEST, SO PLEASE FORGIVE ME.

...HE COULD BE WORTHY OF CARRYING ON YOUR TRADITIONS.

PLEASE, TRAIN HIM.

I'LL HAVE TO CRUSH THE HEAD...

...

IF STABBING IT WON'T WORK...

NN GH

ISN'T THERE ANY WAY TO KILL IT WITH ONE BLOW?

TO COMPLETELY CRUSH THE HEAD, I'LL HAVE TO SMASH IT WITH A ROCK REPEATEDLY.

IT WILL SURELY SUFFER.

SNIFF

WHEN FACING A DEMON, HE STILL REEKS OF SYMPATHY AND CONSIDERATION.

HE EVEN FEELS SYMPATHY FOR A DEMON.

HIS KINDNESS PREVENTS HIM FROM TAKING DECISIVE ACTION.

DAMN...

...THIS KID IS NO GOOD.

I WAS UNCONSCIOUS.

I FEEL SICK.

IS MY BODY DEAD?

...THIS BOY IS USELESS.

GIYU...

WHA-?

...

JUST A TOUCH OF SUNLIGHT DID *THAT?!*

NO WONDER ÑEZUKO FEARS IT!

OH, YEAH...

...THAT GUY.

UM...

HE'S BURYING THE DEMON'S VICTIMS.

WHY COULDN'T YOU ANSWER THAT QUESTION IMMEDIATELY?

...

YOU COULD NEVER FINISH OFF A DEMON BEFORE THE MORNING LIGHT.

YOU STRUGGLE OVER THE SIMPLEST DECISIONS.

YOU ARE TOO *SOFT!*

THAT IS WHAT IT MEANS TO TRAVEL WITH YOUR SISTER WHO HAS BECOME A DEMON!

WHEN YOUR SISTER EATS SOMEONE, THERE ARE *TWO THINGS* YOU HAVE TO DO...

KILL YOUR SISTER... THEN SLIT YOUR OWN *BELLY* AND DIE!

DO YOU UNDER-STAND WHAT I AM SAYING?

YOUR SISTER MUST *NEVER* TAKE THE LIFE...

...OF AN INNOCENT PERSON!

BUT IT IS YOUR SACRED DUTY TO ENSURE THAT THIS *NEVER* HAPPENS.

VERY WELL...

...I WILL TEST YOU TO SEE IF YOU HAVE WHAT IT TAKES...

...TO BE A DEMON-SLAYER SWORDS-MAN.

YES!

SHOULDER YOUR SISTER AND FOLLOW ME.

AND HIS FEET REALLY DON'T MAKE ANY SOUND!

HFF

HFF

HF

HE'S FAST!

HOW OLD IS THIS GUY?!

...SUFFERING IS ALL YOU'VE EVER KNOWN...

BUT THEN...

...LITTLE SISTER.

...THIS'LL BE ROUGH, BUT HANG IN THERE!

NEZUKO...

...TO GIVE THE YOUNGER KIDS PLENTY TO EAT.

INSTEAD, I USE THAT MONEY...

YOU SHOULD BUY A NEW ONE.

ARE YOU MENDING YOUR KIMONO AGAIN?

I LIKE THIS KIMONO!

NO, NO...

...I'M FINE.

EVERYTHING I COULDN'T GIVE TO THEM, I'LL GIVE TO YOU!

AND THEN I'LL BUY YOU A BEAUTIFUL KIMONO!

I WILL MAKE YOU HUMAN AGAIN!

THE TEST *BEGINS* NOW.

CLIMB THE MOUN- TAIN.

...DID I...

...PASS THE TEST?

WHEEZ

WHEEZ

HFF

HFF

S...

SO...

FWIP

HFF

HFF

-I'M DIZZY...

HFF

I'M ALREADY TIRED. MY LEGS ARE GETTING WEAK.

HFF

THIS TIME, I WILL NOT WAIT UNTIL SUNRISE.

NOW YOU MUST DESCEND TO THE HOUSE AT THE FOOT OF THE MOUNTAIN.

HFF

HFF

OH, I GET IT.

HE THINKS I'LL GET LOST IN THIS THICK FOG.

IS THAT ALL?

HFF

HFF

HUH?

I'VE ALREADY MEMORIZED UROKODAKI'S SCENT.

THAT'S EASY! I HAVE A SHARP NOSE!

I JUST HAVE TO GET BACK BEFORE SUNRISE.

HFF

HFF

HFF

I GET IT!

A COVERED PIT!

WSH

UH-OH! HERE WE GO AGAIN!

THESE ARE ALL TRAPS.

THAT'S THE CHALLENGE!

MMPH

HFF

HFF

HFF

IT'S MUCH WORSE THAN THE MOUNTAIN WE LIVED ON!

HFF

...THE AIR'S SO THIN I CAN BARELY BREATHE!

HFF

CONTROL YOUR BREATHING. SNIFF OUT THE TRAPS.

I FEEL LIKE I MIGHT PASS OUT!

NO! I'VE GOTTA GET BACK!

THAT'S WHY I FEEL SO TIRED AND DIZZY.

YES! I CAN SMELL THEM!

TRAPS HAVE TO BE SET BY SOMEONE, AND THOSE SCENTS MUST LINGER.

...THE ABILITY TO EVADE THEM ALL!

BUT KNOWING THEY'RE THERE DOESN'T GRANT ME...

ZZZ

ZZZ

ZZZ

SHMP
SHMP

I...

...MADE IT...

...BACK.

HFF

HFF

HFF

...I ACCEPT YOU AS MY STUDENT!

TANJIRO KAMADO...

Taisho Whispers & Rumors

○ 鬼滅奇譚 (Kimetsu Kitan) (Mysterious Story of the Demon Slayer)

○ 鬼鬼滅滅 (Kikimetsumetsu) (Demon Demon Slayer Slayer)

○ 悪鬼滅々 (Akkimetsumetsu) (Evil Demon Slayer)

○ 鬼殺の刃 (Kisatsu no Yaiba) (Sword of the Demon Killer)

○ 滅々鬼譚 (Metsumetsu Kitan) (Strange Tale of the Demon Slayer)

○ 鬼殺譚 (Kisatsutan) (Tale of the Demon Killer)

○ 空想鬼滅奇譚 (Kuso Kimetsu Kitan) (The Fantastic Strange Tale of the Demon Slayer)

○ 鬼狩リカグツチ (Onigari Kagutsuchi) (Demon Hunting God of Fire)

○ 炭のカグツチ (Sumi no Kagutsuchi) (Charred God of Fire)

* "Kitan" means an unusual and mysterious story.

* "Kagutsuchi" is a god of fire.

Hello, I'm Gotoge.

I hear these titles were under consideration.

Which one do you like?

THEY ARE HUMAN, SO THEIR WOUNDS HEAL SLOWLY AND LOST-LIMBS DO NOT RETURN.

THE DEMON SLAYER CORPS FIGHTS DEMONS FACE-TO-FACE.

NONETHE-LESS, THEY FIGHT DEMONS IN ORDER TO PROTECT ORDINARY PEOPLE.

THERE ARE MANY TRAINERS. IN DIFFERENT PLACES, THEY USE VARIOUS TRAINING METHODS.

I AM A TRAINER.

JUST LIKE IT SOUNDS, I TRAIN SWORDS-MEN.

I DECIDE WHETHER YOU MAY ATTEMPT FINAL SELECTION.

IN ORDER TO JOIN THE DEMON SLAYER CORPS, YOU MUST SURVIVE THE FINAL SELECTION AT MOUNT FUJIKASANE.

AGAIN TODAY, I DESCENDED THE MOUNTAIN.

STARTING TODAY, I HAVE DECIDED TO WRITE THIS JOURNAL FOR NEZUKO.

I TRAIN AS HARD AS I CAN SO I WON'T DIE DURING FINAL SELECTION.

I'M GROWING STRONGER ...

I GO DOWN THE MOUNTAIN REPEATEDLY, DAY AFTER DAY. I'VE BECOME QUITE GOOD AT AVOIDING TRAPS.

...AND MY NOSE IS EVEN SHARPER AT PICKING UP SCENTS.

IT'S LIKE HE REALLY WANTS TO KILL ME.

THOK THOK

BUT THE TRAPS ARE GETTING MUCH DEADLIER.

IT REALLY GETS IN THE WAY...

...SO CARRYING IT GOT ME CAUGHT IN A LOT OF TRAPS.

TODAY, I WENT DOWN THE MOUNTAIN WITH A KATANA.

AFTER DESCENDING THE MOUNTAIN, I SWING THE SWORD SO MUCH I FEEL LIKE MY ARMS MIGHT FALL OFF.

SWSH

SWSH

...715...

...716...

I SAY "TODAY," BUT LATELY I DO THIS EVERY DAY.

TODAY, I PRACTICED SWINGING THE SWORD.

...713...

...714...

WITH A KATANA ...

IT'S STRONG AGAINST FORCE LENGTHWISE BUT WEAK AGAINST FORCE FROM THE SIDE.

THE FIRST THING HE TAUGHT ME WAS THAT A KATANA BREAKS EASILY.

WHEN YOU SWING A KATANA...

...YOU MUST ATTACK STRAIGHT AHEAD.

...THE DIRECTION OF THE BLADE AND THE DIRECTION OF THE FORCE YOU APPLY MUST BE EXACTLY THE SAME.

...HE'LL BREAK MY BONES. HIS THREATS ARE COLD...

...LIKE THE MOUNTAIN.

IN OTHER WORDS, IF I BREAK IT...

... YOU!

FURTHER-MORE...

...IF YOU DAMAGE THE SWORD, HE'LL DAMAGE...

TODAY, I DID NOTHING BUT FALL DOWN...

...TRAINING TO BREAK MY FALL AND GET UP QUICKLY.

URO-KODAKI STANDS AGAINST ME...

...UN-ARMED.

I WIELD MY SWORD AND FACE UROKODAKI WITH THE INTENT TO STRIKE HIM DOWN.

HE EASILY THROWS ME TO THE GROUND.

BUT HE'S RIDICU-LOUSLY STRONG.

HUUUH?!

FWUSH

I'VE BEEN WRIT-ING...

NO!

NO!

THIS?

LIKE THIS?

THIS?

THIS?

NO!

TODAY, I LEARNED BREATHING AND SOME STANDARD FORMS.

...FOR SIX MONTHS, NEZUKO, AND YOU STILL HAVEN'T WOKEN UP.

HE SAID I DIDN'T HAVE ENOUGH STRENGTH IN MY CORE, THEN HE GOT ANGRY AND HIT MY STOMACH.

BAM

AAGH!

BAM

YET IT'S CLEARLY STRANGE FOR YOU TO KEEP SLEEPING LIKE THIS.

UROKODAKI IMMEDIATELY CALLED A DOCTOR TO LOOK AT YOU...

...BUT HE FOUND NOTHING WRONG.

AND...

...THAT'S STILL HOW I FEEL EVERY NIGHT.

I THOUGHT I'D WAKE UP IN THE MORNING TO FIND YOU DEAD.

I WAS SCARED.

MANY TIMES I'VE THOUGHT THAT I WOULD DIE.

AND EVERY DAY I GO HIGHER ON THE MOUNTAIN FOR MY TRAINING, EACH PLACE MORE DANGEROUS AND WITH THINNER AIR.

I HAVE NOTHING MORE TO TEACH YOU.

...THAT WAS ALL HE SAID.

ABOUT A YEAR AFTER I ARRIVED AT MOUNT SAGIRI...

HZZ

HZZ

HFF

HUH?

...TAKE WHAT I HAVE TAUGHT YOU AND BRING IT TO THE NEXT LEVEL?

CAN YOU...

THE REST IS UP TO YOU.

CAN YOU SPLIT IT WITH A KATANA?

CAN THAT EVEN BE SPLIT?!

A BOULDER ....?

THE BLADE WOULD BREAK.

I DON'T THINK I CAN.

UROKO-DAKI!!

UROKO-DAKI!

WAIT! THIS...

STOMP

...HASN'T TAUGHT ME ANYTHING.

... UROKO-DAKI ...

SINCE THAT DAY...

HOLDING MY BREATH, FLEXIBILITY, AND THE MOST BASIC THINGS TOO.

STILL...

...EVERY DAY I PRACTICE WHAT I LEARNED FROM UROKO-DAKI.

I'M GLAD I WROTE EVERYTHING DOWN IN MY JOURNAL.

I'M BEGINNING TO WORRY.

BUT EVEN AFTER HALF A YEAR I STILL CAN'T SPLIT THE BOULDER.

I HAVE TO DO MORE.

MORE!

I HAVEN'T HAD ENOUGH TRAINING.

IT ISN'T ENOUGH.

CHAPTER 5: TANJIRO'S JOURNAL, PART 2

WHAT ARE YOU DOING?

WHERE'D YOU COME FROM?!

!!

HOW LONG DO YOU PLAN TO HAVE YOUR BUTT STUCK IN THE MUD?

TAKE A STANCE!

DOING?

I'M TRAINING.

NOW... ATTACK!

STOMP

...YOU HAVE A WOODEN SWORD AND I HAVE A REAL ONE!

BUT...

HA HA HA HA!

HA HA!

HA HA HA!

YOU'VE GAINED NOTHING. YOU HAVEN'T MASTERED ANYTHING!

YOU SPLIT A BOULDER?!

YOU JUST MEMORIZED IT AS A FACT...

BUT YOUR BODY DOESN'T *UNDER-STAND* ANYTHING!

TOTAL CONCEN-TRATION BREATHING!

CER-TAINLY NOT...

...THE BREATHING TECHNIQUE TAUGHT BY UROKODAKI!

HE KNOWS UROKODAKI?! AND ABOUT THE BREATHING...

!!

THUD

HMM.

FWP

I LEAVE
THE REST
TO YOU.

ARE YOU ALL RIGHT?

DID YOU SEE WHAT HAPPENED?

SH WF

THAT'S HOW I WANT TO BE TOO!

BUT IS THAT EVEN POS-SIBLE?

CAN I DO IT...?

THAT WAS AN INCREDIBLE BLOW!

NOT A BIT OF UNNECES-SARY MOTION!

IT WAS TRULY BEAUTIFUL!

UH... WHO ARE YOU?

SHE'S CUTE...

I'M SURE YOU CAN.

I'LL WATCH OVER YOU.

...AND TELLS ME THE GUY'S NAME IS SABITO.

SHE SAYS HER NAME IS MAKOMO...

SHE CORRECTS MY UNNECESSARY MOVEMENTS AND BAD HABITS.

MAKOMO POINTS OUT THE DEFECTS IN MY STYLE.

I ASK, BUT SHE NEVER TELLS ME.

WHERE DID SHE COME FROM?

WHY IS SHE DOING THIS FOR ME?

SHE OFTEN SAYS THOSE WORDS.

WE REALLY LIKE URO-KODAKI.

THERE ARE OTHER CHILDREN TOO.

THEY AREN'T SIBLINGS. THEY WERE BOTH ORPHANS.

UROKO-DAKI TOOK THEM IN AND RAISED THEM.

THEY'RE ALL AROUND, WATCHING YOU.

TOTAL CONCEN-TRATION BREATH-ING...

...ACCELERATES YOUR BLOOD FLOW AND HEARTBEAT.

AND YOUR TEMPERATURE SHOOTS UP.

MAKOMO IS A BIT OF A STRANGE GIRL.

SHE SAYS THINGS IN A WEIRD WAY.

...AND BRING...

...LOTS OF AIR INTO YOUR BLOOD.

YOU EXPAND YOUR LUNGS...

YOU'RE STILL HUMAN, BUT YOU GET STRONG LIKE A DEMON.

YOUR BLOOD GETS EXCITED AND YOUR BONES AND MUSCLES THRILL.

YOU GET HOT AND STRONG!

HOW CAN THAT BE?

I DON'T REALLY GET IT...

BASICALLY, I DON'T THINK THERE'S ANY-THING ELSE YOU CAN DO.

YOU MUST TRAIN SO HARD THAT YOU COULD DIE.

...BUT... ...AND HEART WOULD BURST IN MY CHEST... ...MY LUNGS... ...AND THAT... ...IT FELT LIKE MY ARMS AND LEGS WOULD COME OFF... ...SO HARD THAT... I SWUNG MY SWORD...

...I STILL COULDN'T BEAT SABITO.

...HE HELD A REAL SWORD. ...WHEN I WENT TO FACE SABITO... ANOTHER SIX MONTHS PASSED. UNTIL ONE DAY...

THE FIGHT WAS OVER IN AN INSTANT.

THAT DAY, IN THAT MOMENT, FOR THE FIRST TIME...

...MY BLADE REACHED SABITO FIRST.

GASP

...OR MAYBE PROUD AND REASSURING.

IT SEEMED LIKE A SAD SMILE TO ME...

WHEN I WON, SABITO SMILED.

SUDDENLY, SABITO DISAPPEARED...

...AGAINST *THEM* TOO.

WIN, TANJIRO...

FWSH

...AND I FOUND THAT MY SWORD HAD NOT CUT SABITO'S MASK.

IT HAD SPLIT THE BOULDER.

WORDS OF GRATITUDE

Thank you to everyone who read this work and to everyone who bought it. Thanks to your support, the series will continue. I can't tell you how thankful I am. Unlike water and food, manga isn't absolutely necessary for survival. Getting you to buy it is a tough job. Thank you very much. I create this manga with the help of many people. I'll work even harder to keep it interesting for you, so please keep reading. And again... thank you!!

Sorry...

I've gotten all your letters. Thank you. They make me so happy, but I can't reply, and that makes me very sorry. Forgive me, please. I'll keep doing my best!

HOWEVER, WHEN USING A NORMAL BLADE, EVEN CUTTING ITS NECK WON'T KILL IT.

A DEMON'S WEAK POINT IS ITS NECK.

THE SWORDS THAT THE DEMON SLAYER CORPS USE ARE MADE FROM A SPECIAL STEEL.

WE CALL THEM NICHIRIN SWORDS.

CHAPTER 6: A MOUNTAIN OF HANDS

WHEN I'M FIGHTING SOME- ONE...

THANKS TO MY TRAINING WITH MAKOMO ...

...I'VE LEARNED TO SMELL OUT AN "OPENING THREAD." THAT'S HOW I WON.

...AND I FIND THAT SCENT, I SEE THE THREAD.

GUIDED BY THE THREAD, MY BLADE CUTS INTO THAT SPOT.

IT RUNS FROM MY BLADE...

...TO A SPOT ON MY OPPONENT, AND IT GOES TAUT THE MOMENT I SEE IT.

I HAD NO WISH TO SEE ANOTHER CHILD DIE.

I DIDN'T THINK YOU WOULD SPLIT THAT BOULDER...

I DID NOT INTEND TO SEND YOU TO FINAL SELECTION.

...BUT YOU DID WELL.

...ARE AN AMAZING CHILD.

TANJIRO...

...YOU...

...BUT BE SURE TO RETURN ALIVE.

GO TO FINAL SELECTION...

YOUR SISTER AND I ARE HERE WAITING.

IT'S CALLED A WARDING MASK.

APPARENTLY, IT OFFERS PROTECTION FROM EVIL.

UROKODAKI GAVE ME A MASK.

AFTER CUTTING MY HAIR...

SO I'M LEAVING HER IN UROKODAKI'S CARE.

I CAN'T TAKE NEZUKO WITH ME—SHE'S STILL ASLEEP.

TANJIRO...

...HOW IS IT YOU...

I'M ON MY WAY, UROKODAKI!

GIVE MY BEST TO SABITO AND MAKOMO!

...KNOW THE NAMES OF THOSE DECEASED CHILDREN?

WOW!

BUT WISTERIA ...

... SHOULDN'T BE BLOOMING THIS TIME OF YEAR.

THE ONE WHO KILLS HIM FIRST GETS TO EAT HIM!

IT'S BEEN SO LONG SINCE I TASTED HUMAN FLESH!

WATER BREATHING!

TOTAL CONCENTRATION...

I'VE GOTTEN STRONGER.

I BEAT TWO DEMONS!

DID IT.

...I CAN DO THIS!

ALL THAT TRAINING WORKED...

REST IN PEACE!

...EVEN THE BONES CRUMBLE!

WHEN I USE THE KATANA THAT URO-KODAKI GAVE ME...

KRRRKSH

WHAT'S THAT ROTTEN SMELL?

UGH!

SNIFF

I'VE NEVER SEEN ANYTHING LIKE IT!

THERE'S A HUGE, DEFORMED DEMON BACK THERE!

THMP

WAAAH!

WHSH

...FOXES HAS COME!

ANOTHER OF MY DEAR...

GLARE

CHAPTER 7: SPIRITS OF THE DECEASED

DO YOU THINK...

...TANJIRO CAN REALLY DO IT?

SABITO ...?

AND YOU KNOW THAT...

...RIGHT?

...NO AMOUNT OF EFFORT IS TOO MUCH.

BUT...

I DON'T KNOW.

LIES!

NO DEMON HERE HAS BEEN ALIVE THAT LONG!

YOU'RE LYING!

DEMON HUNTER... EDO PERIOD?!

PLUS, THE DEMONS EAT EACH OTHER TOO!

...AND THEY GET KILLED DURING SELECTION!

THEY ONLY PUT DEMONS UP HERE THAT HAVE EATEN TWO OR THREE PEOPLE...

...I HAVE EATEN 50 OF YOU BRATS!

...OF WISTERIA BLOSSOMS...

BUT I HAVE SURVIVED A VERY LONG TIME. IN THIS PRISON...

...A DEMON'S STRENGTH COMES FROM THE NUMBER OF PEOPLE IT HAS CONSUMED.

REMEMBER...

FIFTY?!

...AND SOME PHYSICALLY CHANGE, GAINING UNNATURAL POWERS.

THAT'S RIGHT. THEY GROW STRONGER...

IF IT EATS MANY PEOPLE IT GETS STRONGER?

...HOW MANY PEOPLE A DEMON HAS EATEN.

IF YOUR NOSE GETS STRONGER YOU'LL BE ABLE TO TELL...

?!

WHAT ARE YOU TALKING ABOUT?

...YOU ARE NUMBER 14.

...12...

...13...

...AND...

I'VE DECIDED TO KILL *ALL* OF HIS STUDENTS!

THAT'S HOW MANY OF *UROKODAKI'S STUDENTS* I HAVE EATEN!

HEE HEE

HEE HEE

HEE

THE OTHER WAS A GIRL-BRAT WHOSE KIMONO WAS COVERED IN FLOWERS.

HE HAD A COLORFUL JACKET, AND WAS THE STRONGEST BY FAR.

SHE WAS SMALL AND NOT SO STRONG...

...BUT SHE WAS VERY AGILE.

HE HAD PEACH-COLORED HAIR AND A SCAR BY HIS MOUTH.

THIRTEEN OF URO-KADAKI'S STUDENTS, BUT ABOVE ALL...

YES, INDEED!

...TWO OF THEM...

...I'LL NEVER FORGET.

HOW COULD THIS DEMON HAVE KILLED THEM? THEY TRAINED ME!

I KNOW THE GRAIN OF THOSE MASKS THAT UROKO-DAKI CARVES.

THEY'RE CARVED THE SAME WAY AS THE TENGU MASK HE WORE.

I RECOGNIZE YOU...

...BY THOSE FOX MASKS.

THEY'RE ALL INSIDE MY STOMACH.

IT'S LIKE UROKODAKI FED THEM TO ME!

HFF

HFF

HFF

DID HE CALL IT A "WARDING MASK"?

I ATE THEM ALL *BECAUSE* OF THE MASKS THEY WORE.

THE GIRL-BRAT WEPT AND GREW ANGRY WHEN I TOLD HER THAT.

HEH HEH HEH HEH...

HEH HEH...

HEH HEH HEH HEH...

WAKE UP, BIG BROTHER!

WHS

WHAM

BAM

A STRANGE SMELL FROM THE GROUND!

NO MATTER HOW MANY ARMS I CUT OFF, IT GROWS MORE!

HUH ?!

THE FOX-BRAT IS IN STRIKING RANGE!

I CAN'T GROW MORE IN TIME!

AND I'M OUT OF HANDS!

HE ESCAPED!

WATER BREATHING!

TOTAL CONCENTRATION.

EVEN THE PEACH-HAIR COULDN'T CUT IT!

BUT MY NECK IS HARD AND IMPERVIOUS!

...AND CRUSH IT, JUST LIKE I DID TO THE OTHER ONE!

WHEN HE FAILS TO CUT MY NECK, I'LL GRAB HIS HEAD...

SNIFF

YOU'RE READING THE
WRONG WAY!

DEMON SLAYER: KIMETSU NO YAIBA reads from right to left, starting in the upper-right corner. Japanese is read from right to left, meaning that action, sound effects and word-balloon order are completely reversed from English order.